MY TEDDY BEAR

AT PLAY

Teddy Bear and his friends the toys are in the garden. The sun is shining. Teddy Bear and Toy Soldier are playing catch with a shiny red ball. Back and forth, they throw the ball, high up in the air. Toy Soldier throws it so high that he doesn't see the fat cat behind him, and he trips over his tail!

Rag Doll and Clown are sitting on the garden swing. They are playing a game of 'I spy'. Clown has to find a word beginning with the letter 's'. Could it be snail, or spade? 'No, that's not the word,' says Rag Doll. 'The right word is shoe.' Teddy has found something beginning with the letter 's' as well.

All of the toys enjoy taking it in turns to skip

over a rope. Rag Rabbit and Wooden Doll are

turning the rope for Teddy Bear. Rag Rabbit is

very small and he can't get the rope high

enough. Teddy has caught his leg in the rope

and has fallen into the flowers. 'Are you

alright, Teddy?' asks his friend the Clown.

It's started to rain. The sky is very dark, and it looks like it is going to last for quite a long time. The toys are hurrying indoors. Teddy Bear is helping Wooden Duck and Rag Rabbit. They can't run as fast as the others. They are all getting soaked through, and they are very miserable because the rain has spoiled all the fun they were having.

Indoors it is nice and dry. The toys have decided to play hide-and-seek, and they have chosen Teddy to be 'It'. Teddy has to count to twenty, and then he has to search every room in the house until he finds them. Teddy doesn't mind being the one who has to search. His friends are not very good at hiding, and it is always easy to find them.

After hide-and-seek, Rag Doll teaches Teddy

and Clown how to make a jigsaw puzzle. It is

very easy. Rag Doll has found a nice picture of

a car in an old magazine. She has glued the

picture onto a piece of cardboard, and now

she is cutting the cardboard into lots of

different shapes that Teddy and Clown can

make up into a picture again.

Rag Elephant would rather ride in a car than make jigsaw puzzles out of pictures of them.

He has found some old boxes, and he has painted wheels, headlights, and a number plate onto them. He could not find anything to use as a steering wheel, so he is using an old cushion. Rag Rabbit is just putting the finishing touches to the bonnet, and off they'll go!

Teddy and Rag Doll like to play with building blocks. Teddy is building a wall with cubes, and Rag Doll is building a tall tower out of lots of different shapes. Rag Doll has to stand on the tip of her toes to reach up high enough. She has to keep her hand very still so that the last block will balance on the top.

All of the toys like to play blindman's buff. It is Clown's turn to wear the spotted blindfold. They are all running around Clown and teasing him, because they know he is not very good at this game. Rag Rabbit has just thrown a balloon to Clown. Poor Clown thinks he has caught Teddy by the ears! The toys think this game is great fun.

The toys are too tired to play any more. They sit down in front of the fire. Soon it will be teatime.

They spend a little while looking at favourite picture books. 'Hooray!' cries Toy Soldier, 'The sun is beginning to come out again.' Sure enough, the rain begins to stop, and through the window, the toys can soon see a lovely rainbow, as the sun comes back out again.